Tall Body, Short Body, Everybody's Somebody

Tall Body, Short Body, Everybody's Somebody

Mary Hollingsworth

Illustrated by Daniel J. Hochstatter
& Dennis Edwards

CPH
Concordia Publishing House

Tall body,
Short body,
Everybody's
Somebody.

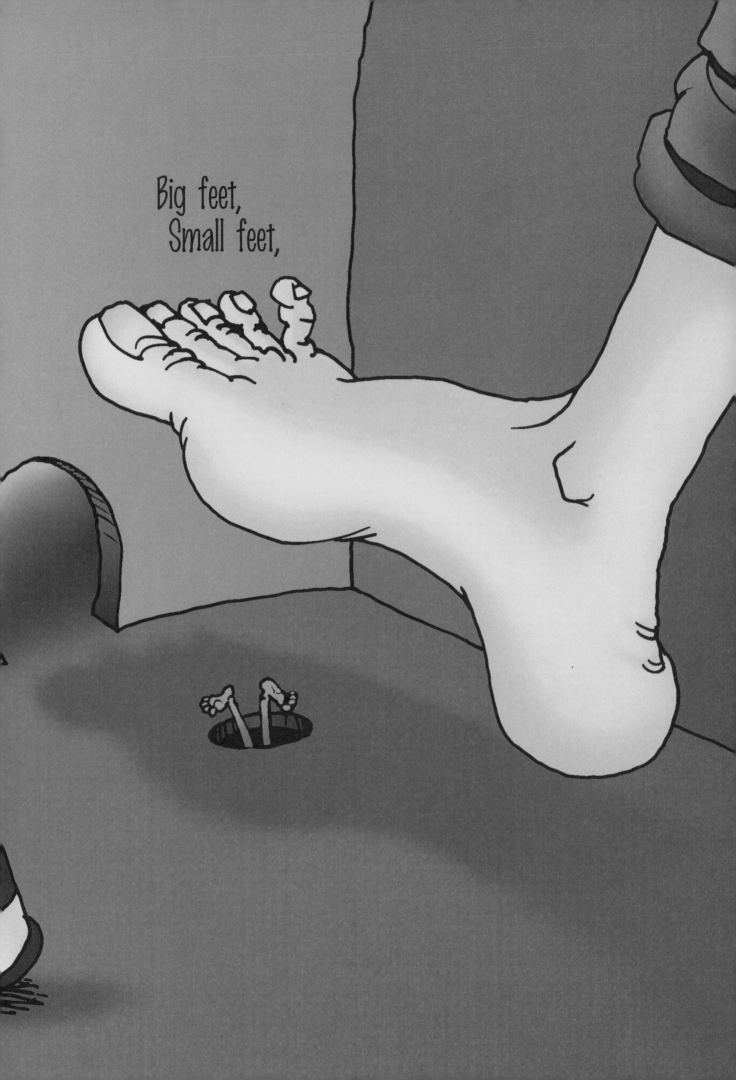

Careful feet
Are happy
feet.

Brown arms,
White arms,
Yellow, red,
And black arms.

Strong arms,
Weak arms—
All arms
Are hugging arms.

Hooked nose?
Straight nose?
Who knows?
God knows.

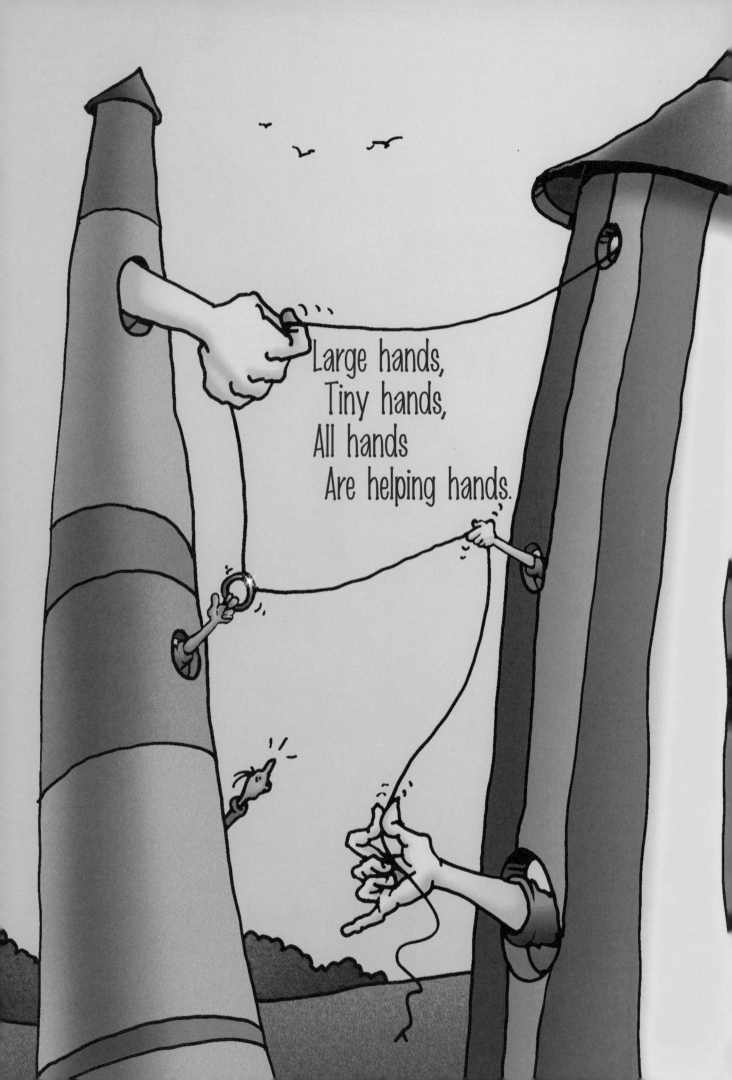

Large hands,
Tiny hands,
All hands
Are helping hands.

Brown hair,
Blonde hair,
Red hair,
Gray hair,

Long legs,
Short legs,

Happy heart?
Broken heart?
Do your part
To mend a heart.

Different folks?
That's all right!

We are different
But the same;
For each of us
Jesus came.

Brown eyes,
Blue eyes,

Green eyes—
  Close your eyes.

    Ice creams,
      Moonbeams—
        May your dreams
        Be happy dreams.

Nite, nite.
Sleep tight.
Angels guard you
Through the night.